Squirrels in the Garden

written and illustrated by

Olive L. Earle

William Morrow & Company
New York   1963

In early spring two little gray squirrels were born in a hole high up in a tree. At first they were quite helpless. They were blind and, except for some soft little whiskers near the mouth, they were without hair. Each tiny front foot had four prickles on it and each tiny back foot had five; these prickles would be claws someday.

The babies got milk from their mother's nipples. All animals that get their first food in this way belong to the mammal group. Elephants are mammals and so, too, are people.

The leaves, the paper, and the strips of soft bark that lined the nest hole helped to keep the naked babies warm. Earlier in the season the mother squirrel had carried big mouthfuls of dry leaves and bark to the nest, which was thirty feet from the ground. And somehow she had managed to climb up to it with a great wad of newspaper in her mouth. Even though she held the bedding very high, it made awkward bundles to carry up the tree trunk.

The gray squirrel parents had mated forty-four days before the babies were born. The father had gone away before their birth, but their mother took affectionate care of them. She was thin, and while she was nursing the babies she needed more food than usual. She ate all the seeds she could find, as well as many tender twigs and buds of elm, maple, and other trees. And when the catkins of oak flowers blossomed, she liked them too.

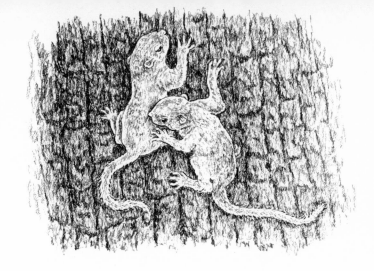

The baby squirrels grew quite slowly, and it was not until they were ten days old that enough hair had sprouted to make their skin look grayish. At the end of three weeks they were well covered with soft hair. Their front teeth began to poke through then, too. But their eyes remained shut until the babies were five weeks old.

All went well in the nursery until, one day, a great windstorm blew down the tree in which the family lived. The squirrels

were unhurt, but the broken tree could no longer be used as a home. The mother had to find another shelter, and she knew of one. It was a hole high under the eaves of a big house that was not too far away. There was only an outside entrance to the hole; the inside of the house could not be reached from it. There was no chance that the growing babies would go exploring and get lost in the house.

Now the trip to the new home had to be made. Mother Squirrel picked up a baby and started off. She did not carry him by the back of his neck, the way a cat carries a kitten, but gently grasped in her mouth a fold of skin on his underside. The baby, by now six weeks old and quite furry, twisted his fluffy little tail around her neck. In safety, she

carried him down the road and across a large garden. She climbed a wisteria vine, which formed a convenient ladder to the roof of the house. Then, with a twist of her body, she swung over the gutter and into the hole.

Leaving the first baby in his new home, Mother Squirrel fetched the second one. Then she went back a third time to the fallen tree and looked in the old hole. Apparently she could not count, and she wanted to be sure that no little squirrel had been left behind. Sometimes a squirrel mother may have six babies, and in southern areas two sets of babies may be born each year.

Empty-mouthed, Mother Squirrel returned to the house in the garden. There she found that some peanuts had been thrown on the path for her. Quickly she grabbed one and went off in a leaping run. Squirrels' back legs are much longer than their front ones, and often the animal moves over the ground in a series of leaps.

With the peanut in her mouth, Mother Squirrel jumped onto the top of a tree stump and sat back on her hindquarters with her tail shading her back. She belonged to a group of animals called, by zoologists, *Sciuridae* (pronounced Si-u'-ri-dee). This family name means *shade tail*.

Holding the peanut in her forepaws, the hungry mother gnawed through the brittle shell in no time at all and got at the nut inside. She was a rodent, or gnawing animal, and her upper front teeth were as sharp as chisels. A rodent's teeth grow, from the base, all the time. The enamel on the back is softer than that on the front, so it wears away readily. Because of this wearing away, a rodent's teeth are sharpened when it gnaws hard food.

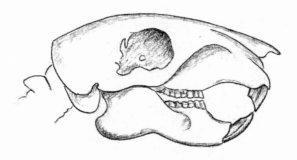

Mother Squirrel ate a great many peanuts. At last, her hunger satisfied, she picked up in her mouth the only remaining one and ran across the lawn to the wild part of the garden. With her nose she poked the peanut into the soft earth, and then scraped leaves over the spot. Her keen sense of smell might enable her to find it later on. Often squirrels do not find their hidden nuts and acorns, and some of them grow into trees. A tiny horsechestnut tree nearby had sprouted from a seed she had once buried there. The blue jays in the garden had similar tree-planting habits, and there were many seedling trees in the wild area.

Well fed, Mother Squirrel took a long drink from the birds' pan of water just after a garter snake had had a bath in it. Then she returned to her tree stump. She sat on her haunches with her front feet pressed against her white chest. After looking this way and that for a possible enemy—a hawk

might be soaring overhead looking for a meal—she groomed her coat with rapid scratches of a hind foot. Then she polished her head with a front foot.

Her beauty treatment completed, she scampered up the trunk of a tree that grew close to the house. Part way up she became alarmed when she saw a dog on the garden path. In squirrel manner, she skittered to the far side of the tree trunk so that she was out of sight. A moment later she was in front again, hurrying up the tree and onto a branch. The dog wandered near and, from her safe perch, she scolded with short excited noises, *"Chak! Chak! Chak! A-a-a!"*

Then, with her voice going higher the angrier she got, she chattered, *"Chirr! Chirr! Chirr!"* She made a kind of mewing sound too. All the while she lashed her tail from side to side, or held it stiff with its tip twitching. The dog, intent on his own business, went on his way without paying any attention to the furious little animal.

The dog gone, Mother Squirrel soon calmed down. She decided to take a sun bath before going back to the nursery. She flattened herself along a branch, so that she looked more like a squirrel skin spread there than a round-bodied creature.

Warmed and rested, Mother Squirrel made a three-foot leap from the tip of the branch to the roof of the house. In a flash, she reached the nursery and her hungry babies.

By the time they were two months old, the young squirrels had gained strength and confidence. Two small heads with big eyes could often be seen poking out from the hole under the eaves. One of the babies seemed to look with interest at the big world below, but his little brother seemed timid and shy.

While Skippy, the bold baby, and his brother, the shy one, were growing, so were the tendrils of the wisteria vine. The new leaves were now within a few inches of the nest's opening. When a breeze blew a tendril close enough, Skippy, hanging on tight to the hole's rim with his back feet, made a grab for it with his front paws. Holding fast to the swaying vine, with his body stretched its full length, he ate the tender leaves. He tried to reach some more of them, although the wind was blowing the vine farther away.

Then little Skippy found he could not move. Stretched out as he was, he dared not go forward, and he could not pull himself back into the hole again. His muscles were not strong enough to hold his body suspended in mid-air, and down he fell into the vine's thick foliage below. Unhurt, he managed to gain a foothold quickly. But he was scared and he squeaked unhappily. His mother heard him and, hurrying to a low branch of the nearby tree, she called to him with a kind of scolding chatter. Then she jumped to the vine and led him slowly up its strong stem to the safety of the roof.

Skippy crouched beside his mother on the roof's edge. When he seemed to have recovered from his fright, she began to lead him back and forth along the roof. At last she seemed satisfied that he was sure-footed enough for further adventure, and she jumped from the roof to a branch of the tree. Skippy watched, but apparently was afraid to follow her. She jumped back beside him, then to the tree once more. Time and again she leaped back and forth. At last Skippy gained courage and made the jump.

Confidently, as though he had done it all his life, Skippy clutched a small branch and clung to it. He kept his balance by moving his tail from side to side. His instinct made him use it this way, for he was born know-

ing how to do many things that all squirrels before him have done.

Carefully, step by step, the little squirrel followed his mother down the tree trunk. His sharp claws enabled him to cling to the rough bark. He climbed down head first, not backwards as a cat does.

Once on the ground, he frisked gaily over the lawn. Sometimes he ran along on all four feet, and sometimes he made short leaps with his front feet barely touching the grass. Nothing seemed to escape his attention, whether it was a tender shoot that had to be sniffed and might be good to eat, or the sight of his mother stretching up to bite off a tulip. He skipped aside when a

fearless mourning dove, squatting on the lawn, pecked at him. He seemed to be glad to be out of the dark hole under the eaves.

In the tree above him Skippy heard the mewing call of a catbird. Then he saw his mother climbing up to the spreading branches of a tall shrub. There, about eight feet from the ground and almost hidden by leaves, was the catbird's nest with four greenish-blue eggs in it. The bird, knowing that squirrels occasionally steal eggs or baby

birds, scolded noisily, *"Miouw! Miouw!"*
Though smaller than a robin, the catbird
was not afraid of the squirrel and flew down
to attack the nest robber. Mother Squirrel

did not like the swoops made at her head,
and she decided to leave the nest alone.

She jumped from the bush and scampered away, with Skippy racing after her.

After an active morning in the garden, Skippy found himself at the base of the wisteria vine. He ran up it and discovered that it led him to the roof. He found the entrance to his home without trouble and went into the hole.

The next morning his shy brother followed him safely out of the nursery. The two frolicked together on the ground. They chased each other up the tree. Skippy dodged to the far side of the trunk as though to hide, then peeked at his brother, who waited a moment before scurrying after him. Apparently they were practicing the squirrel trick of always running to the far side of a tree trunk when they think they are being watched.

Growing bolder, the young squirrels explored the upper branches of the tree where they knew, by instinct, that a small twig should be tested before weight was put on it. Soon they would learn a safe path through the treetops so they could dash full tilt from branch to branch when necessary.

While touring the garden one day, Skippy discovered a heavy wire that was being used to brace a small tree. It stretched from the small tree to a larger one so that it made a tightrope all ready for a young acrobat to use. Skippy found that he could walk along it by using his tail to keep him right side

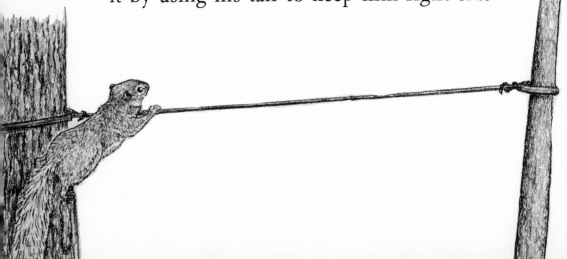

up. Fearful at first, he gained courage and ran part way along the wire. Then he stopped. Suddenly he twirled, heels over head, around the wire. Over and over, around and around he went. Then, seemingly pleased with his gymnastics, he finished his trip along the wire. He jumped down and went to join his brother.

Skippy grew more and more adventurous as the days went by. He investigated the porch, with its long glass door. The glass confused him; he did not seem to understand why he could not pass through it. He scratched at it and pushed at it with his nose for minutes at a time. Then one day

he found the door open. There was nothing to stop him now, and into the room he scampered to explore every corner. Suddenly, in the doorway, a puppy stood barking at him. Scared, Skippy crouched behind a chair until the yapping puppy was carried away. Then he made a wild dash—out of the door, across the porch, and up the vine to the safety of his home. He did not try to get inside the house again.

By July, the weather had turned very
warm. This was the time of year when the
squirrels' coats were thin and their tails
much less bushy. Skippy and his family no
longer slept in the hot hole under the eaves,
but found a cooler shelter. After repairing
it, they moved into a huge leaf house that
had been built and used before by other
squirrels. It was in the fork of a tree and
was about fifty feet above the ground. Made
with great skill, it had a platform of twigs
covered by a rain-shedding mound of leaves,

dried grasses, and small twigs. A door on the side led to a room lined with soft grass, which was about sixteen inches across and twelve inches in height.

The squirrels left their den to forage and play in the cool morning hours and in the late afternoon. Occasionally, when the full moon lit up the garden so that it was almost as light as day, the squirrels went out at night. Skippy was exploring a nearby wooded area on one such trip when he saw a flying squirrel. This little creature, smaller than Skippy, stayed in his hole during the

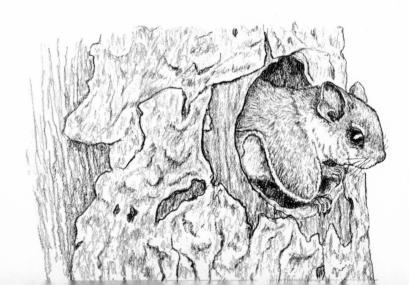

day, but was very active at night. He could not really fly, in spite of his name; instead he glided from a high branch to a low one or to the ground. To glide, he leaped from a height and immediately spread the fold of skin that stretched along his sides between each front and hind foot. This spread skin formed a parachute that could bear him safely on a glide of well over one hundred feet.

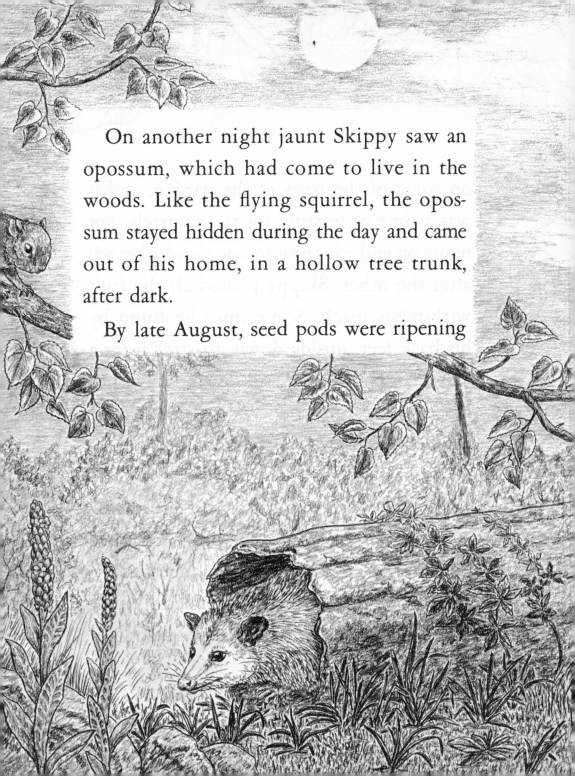

On another night jaunt Skippy saw an opossum, which had come to live in the woods. Like the flying squirrel, the opossum stayed hidden during the day and came out of his home, in a hollow tree trunk, after dark.

By late August, seed pods were ripening

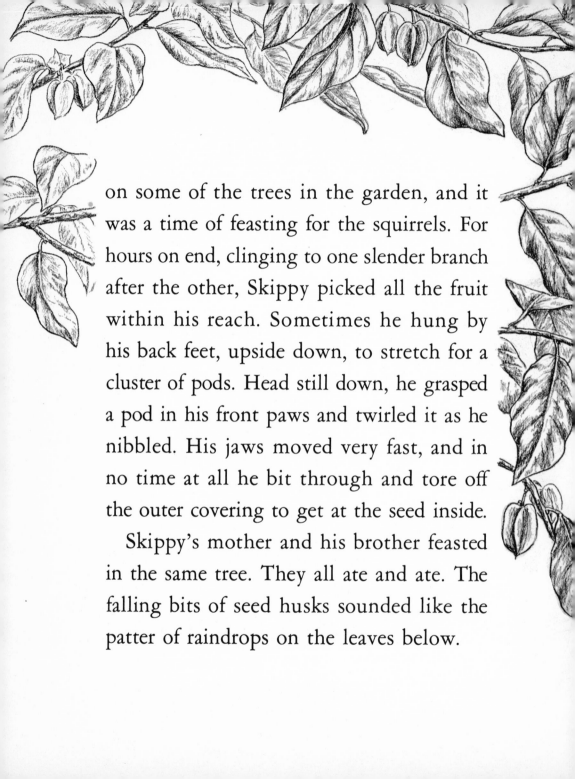

on some of the trees in the garden, and it
was a time of feasting for the squirrels. For
hours on end, clinging to one slender branch
after the other, Skippy picked all the fruit
within his reach. Sometimes he hung by
his back feet, upside down, to stretch for a
cluster of pods. Head still down, he grasped
a pod in his front paws and twirled it as he
nibbled. His jaws moved very fast, and in
no time at all he bit through and tore off
the outer covering to get at the seed inside.

Skippy's mother and his brother feasted
in the same tree. They all ate and ate. The
falling bits of seed husks sounded like the
patter of raindrops on the leaves below.

When Skippy was not eating or resting, he was making trips all around the neighborhood. Sometimes he used the telephone wire as a highway, balancing himself easily on the thin cable as he ran along it. One day he made a tour of the vacant lot next door, and from there wandered into another garden. He jumped to the rim of its swimming pool, sat back on his haunches, and

looked around. The squirrels in the garden
did not go readily into water. But Skippy
now learned, the hard way, that he could
swim well. A stupid boy threw a large stone
at him—and hit him. Into the water the
squirrel fell with a splash. Frightened, but

paddling actively with all four feet, he swam around and around the pool. Almost exhausted, he at last managed after several tries to clamber up onto a small raft. He looked, terrified, in all directions. Then he gathered his courage and took a long leap to the rim of the pool. Without even waiting to shake his wet fur, he made off as fast as he could go. Soon he was back in his own garden, where he sat on a tree stump in the warm sun until he was dry.

The weeks went by and Skippy grew fat
on acorns and other tree seeds. He enjoyed
dogwood berries and mushrooms, too. And
when he found an insect cocoon, he ate that.
He stored some nuts by burying them about
an inch deep, each in a separate place. He
also saved food for future use by tucking it
into the crevices in a tree's bark.

Now Skippy was ready to face the cold days ahead. He was not yet quite as big as his mother, for squirrels do not reach their full growth until their second year. Next year Skippy would measure about twenty or more inches from nose to tail tip, with his tail making up half his length. And he would weigh up to one and a half pounds. Barring an accident, he would live to be at least ten years old.

By the time winter came, Skippy seemed to have outgrown his nickname, Now his family name *Sciuridae* fitted him well, and so he was known as Shade Tail. His tail almost covered his body when he curved it over his back. The white-tipped, blackish-

gray hair on it had grown long and was
bushy, instead of being scanty as it had been
in midsummer. The coat of thick, dark gray
hair on his back had a rusty sheen to it. His
sides, legs, and head were a paler gray, and
his underparts were white. (Occasionally a
gray squirrel does not fit his name, for he
will be all black instead of gray. And, rarely,
a gray squirrel is all white.)

Shade Tail needed a heavy coat, because he would be out looking for food in all but the worst weather. He was not a hibernating animal—that is, he did not spend the winter hidden away in a kind of sleep, as some animals do. The bats, for instance, which had flitted about the garden in the

dusk of the summer evenings, found a shel-
tered spot and were torpid throughout the
winter.

The snows came. When a storm was over, Shade Tail was out sniffing for the nuts and acorns he had buried earlier. The fresh snow on the ground became patterned with his tracks. The imprint left by each front foot showed only four claw marks, because the remnant of an inner toe—the "thumb" of long-ago squirrels—was small, high on the foot, and had no claw. But each hind foot left a track with five claw marks. When leaping along, the squirrel's front feet hit the ground first and the back feet swung

forward to overtake them. The tracks of the
back feet then were ahead of those of the
front feet. When Shade Tail traveled at high
speed, the sets of tracks were as much as
twenty-four inches apart.

Shade Tail did not seem to care if he could not find some of his stored food, for there was always a meal awaiting him on the porch. There he kept well fed on nuts, a dried ear of corn, peanuts, or even bits of dry toast. He drank from the birds' water pan. In a short time, he quite lost his wildness and would try to reach for food held in an outstretched hand. But he was not allowed to take it; it was thrown to him in-

stead. This was done because, by accident, he might have nipped a finger, and a squirrel bite can be dangerous. Soon Shade Tail became so tame that he would explore a person's coat pocket in the hope of finding a nut.

Not content with his own food, Shade Tail sometimes raided the birds' feeding tray. No one was pleased with him when he took the redbirds' sunflower seeds, or when he stole the peanut butter and suet cakes provided for the chickadees, nuthatches, and other birds.

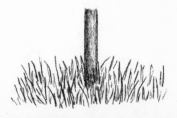

His mother, his brother, and visiting
squirrels also came to the porch for food.
They never quarreled, and several of them
slept together in the hole under the eaves,
which they had relined with dry leaves.

At last the worst of the winter was over. Shade Tail seemed to feel quite grown up and acted as though it would soon be time to choose a mate. A young visiting squirrel felt restless too, and when he met Shade Tail on a branch one day, a fight began. The two squirrels bit and clawed at each other.

Sure-footed though they ordinarily were, each lost his grip on the small branch as the battle raged. They tumbled to the ground, but that did not stop the fight. Over and over they rolled, with first one

and then the other on top. At last Shade Tail got the best of it and his enemy gave up. Battered and subdued, the defeated squirrel ran away. Shade Tail bore a sign of the fight all his life, for one of his ears had been torn and its split edge never joined together.

Twigs were now getting green. The squirrels who had fed on the porch could get other food, so they went away. Shade Tail roamed about the neighborhood looking for an attractive female. Soon he found one and chose her for his mate. But, as is natural for squirrels, he did not stay with her long and went off in search of further adventures.

Shade Tail's mate put new nesting material in the hole under the eaves of the house in the garden. There, early in the spring, her four babies were born. When they grew up they looked just like Shade Tail.

by the same author

BIRDS AND THEIR NESTS
BIRDS OF THE CROW FAMILY
CAMELS AND LLAMAS
CRICKETS
MICE AT HOME AND AFIELD
THE OCTOPUS
PAWS, HOOFS, AND FLIPPERS
PIGS, TAME AND WILD
ROBINS IN THE GARDEN
STATE BIRDS AND FLOWERS
STATE TREES
THE SWANS OF WILLOW POND
WHITE PATCH, A CITY SPARROW